The Rising Butterfly

written by
Abigail Beaudry

illustrated by
Lewis Walton

My name is Abigail Beaudry and I have Autism. I wrote this book to give a glimpse of what it was like for me growing up with Autism and how I felt invisible. Each day continues to bring new adventures and challenges, but I just keep striving to overcome it all in my own unique way.

I wrote this book to inspire others like me who have Autism and to inspire others who sometimes just felt like I did...invisible. I want you all to know you are special and amazing just the way you are. I see you! So just continue to do your best, because that is the best you can do. You are like a butterfly, so spread your beautiful wings and fly! I hope my story can help bring understanding, awareness and acceptance that no matter who we are or what struggles we have, we all just want to be included and accepted. When it comes down to it, we just want to be a friend and have a friend.

I would like to express my Thanks to the late Mr. Thomas Marcello who helped me find my courage through theatre, Mr. Neil Jeronimo for inspiring me to be vulnerable with my feelings, Mr. Steven Manchester for being my mentor and guiding me through the process of becoming an author. Dreams do come true!

To my step-father Lewis Walton, I thank you for always taking the time to see into my world and knowing me so well that you are able to capture my story through your illustrations. You brought my words to life! I also want to say Thank You to my beautiful mom, Vivianne Walton and brother Tyler Beaudry for their endless love and support throughout this project. You are my biggest advocates and cheerleaders. I love you all.

I must also Thank the countless teachers, friends and adults who saw me when I believed no one could and who touched my life, helping me become the person I am today. I will never forget you!

I dedicate this book to ALL of you!

When I was young, it was hard making friends....

Everyone seemed to know how
to fit in perfectly...

Watching the world around me awaken with so muchactivity was exciting...

But I felt like I was not a part of it all…….

The thought of being invisible was really scary to me,
it was like being trapped in a box...

I wanted to be noticed
and accepted.....

Finding out I had Autism
made me feel selfconscious
and different....

I finally realized it is ok, Autism
does not define me,
I just accomplish things in my
own unique way......

I am trying to fit in just like everyone else.....

It doesn't change who I am…..

The dreams I have.......

Or the goals I set for myself...

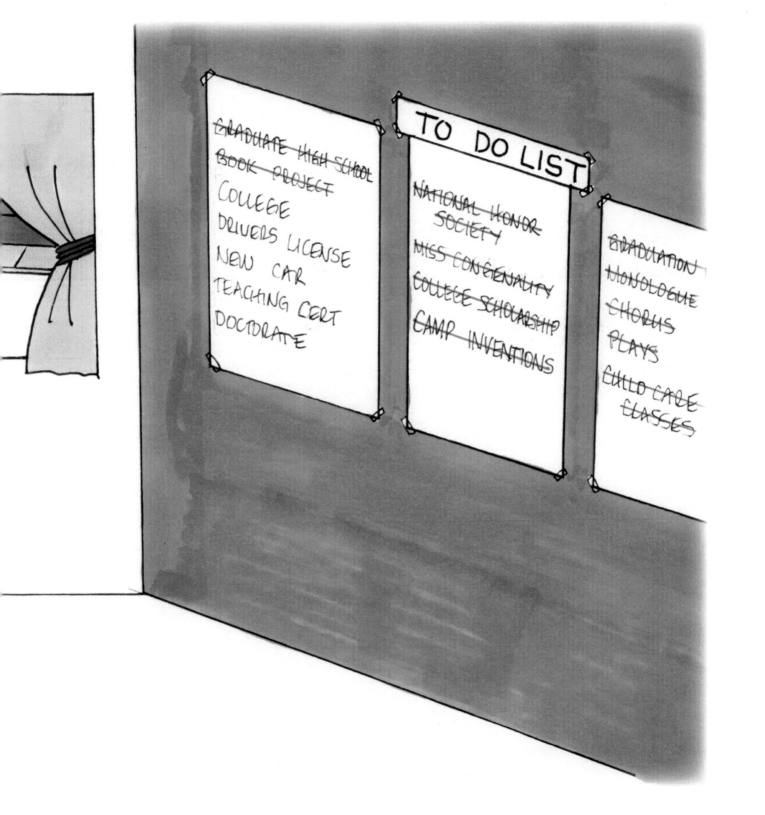

Life is a journey and I refuse to be invisible...

First I had to sprout...

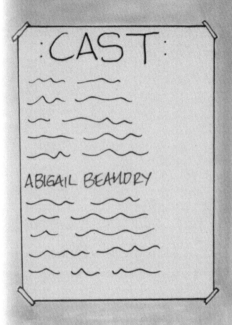

Then I had to blossom...

Now I am a confident
social butterfly...

Who is spreading her wings and flying!

I am a Butterfly!

Abigail is a vibrant and energetic girl, who always sees the positive in everything. She was inspired to write this book based on her first-hand experiences and emotions, growing up as a young girl with Autism. Finding inspiration from those around her, she has decided to never let Autism define her.

She wants her story to help others and give them inspiration. Her message is to never stop spreading your wings toward reaching your goals...and to always fly, no matter the challenges. Abigail currently lives in a small town in Massachusetts with her mom, step-father, 7 cats, 2 birds and a dog. She has a brother—whom she adores—who is serving as a Combat Medic for the U.S. Army. Currently, she is attending college for Early Childhood Education and hopes to become a teacher someday. She also hopes to help other students like her to realize that they are capable of so much, and that the only limits they have are the ones they put on themselves. Abigail enjoys drawing, singing, writing and being involved in Theatre. In her free time, she loves to go camping, take road trips and make videos for Youtube. She is currently working on a short cartoon with her step-father, planning to finish it sometime next year.

More than anything, she hopes you enjoy her book and that it brings comfort and inspiration because we all are Rising Butterflies...